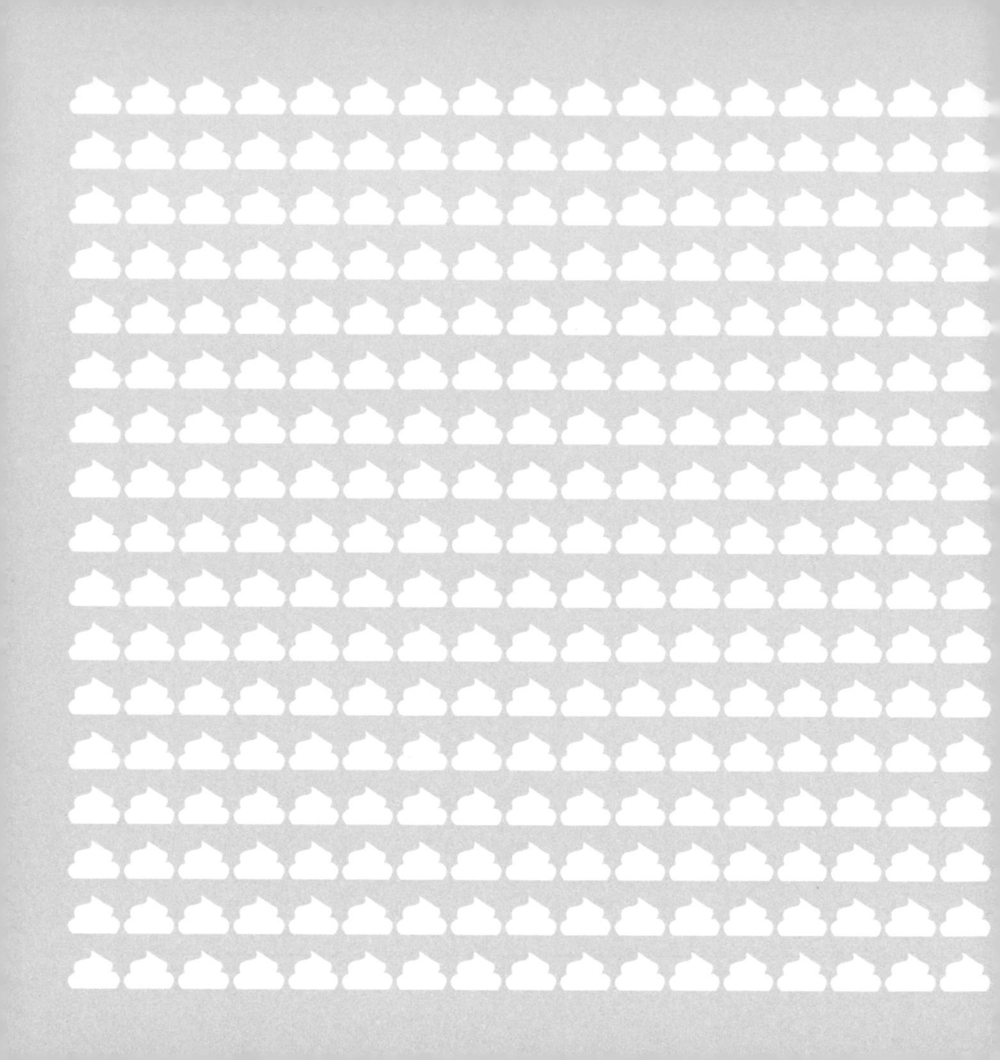

52 THINGS TO DO WHILE YOU POO

52 THINGS TO DO WHILE YOU POO

AN HACHETTE UK COMPANY
WWW.HACHETTE.CO.UK

SUMMERSDALE PUBLISHERS LTD
PART OF OCTOPUS PUBLISHING GROUP LIMITED
CARMELITE HOUSE
50 VICTORIA EMBANKMENT
LONDON
EC4Y 0DZ
UK

WWW.SUMMERSDALE.COM
PRINTED AND BOUND IN MALTA
ISBN: 978-1-84953-497-0

TO MY WIFE AND KIDS, FOR ALWAYS BEING THERE, UNTIL THEY HAD TO LEAVE THE ROOM

HUGH JASSBURN HAS BEEN POOING SINCE 1974. AFTER SEVERAL MONTHS OF PRODUCING A VARIETY OF STOOLS (MOSTLY IN WASHABLE AND REUSABLE NAPPIES) HE MOVED ON TO DISPOSABLES. BY 1978 HUGH WAS A REGULAR TOILET USER AND HASN'T LOOKED BACK SINCE. HIS FAVOURED POSITION IS WITH HIS BACK TO THE CISTERN, BOTH FEET PLANTED FIRMLY ON THE GROUND AND BOTH ELBOWS RESTING ON HIS KNEES. HE FLUSHES WHEN HE'S STANDING, IS NOT A FAN OF CHEAP TOILET PAPER AND STRONGLY BELIEVES THE FLAP SHOULD ALWAYS BE AT THE FRONT OF THE ROLL.

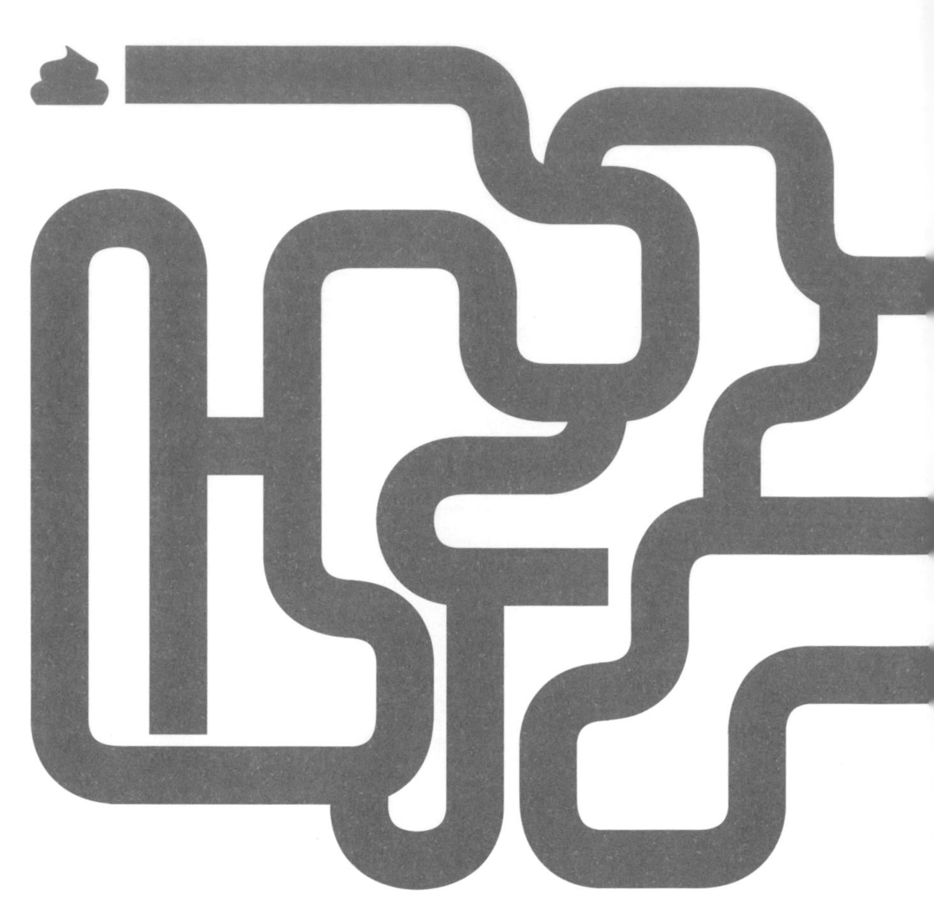

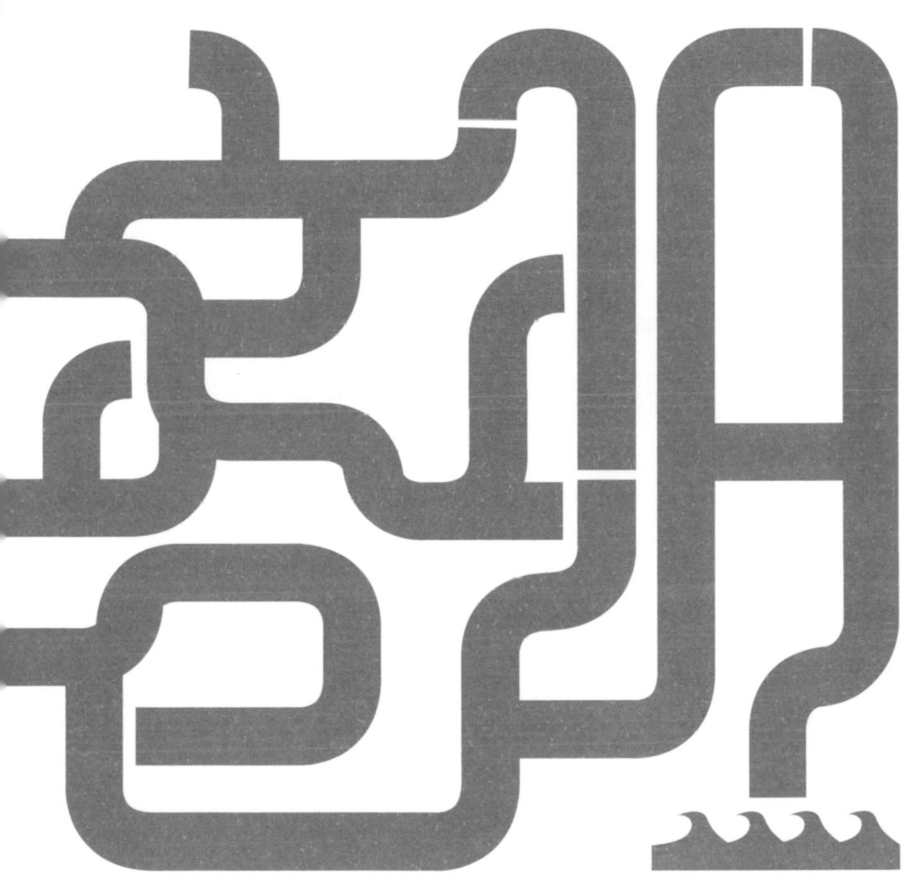

... WHILE YOU POO

POO FACT
70% WATER
10% INDIGESTIBLE FOOD
10% DEAD BACTERIA
10% FATS, SALTS, LIVE BACTERIA, DEAD CELLS, MUCUS

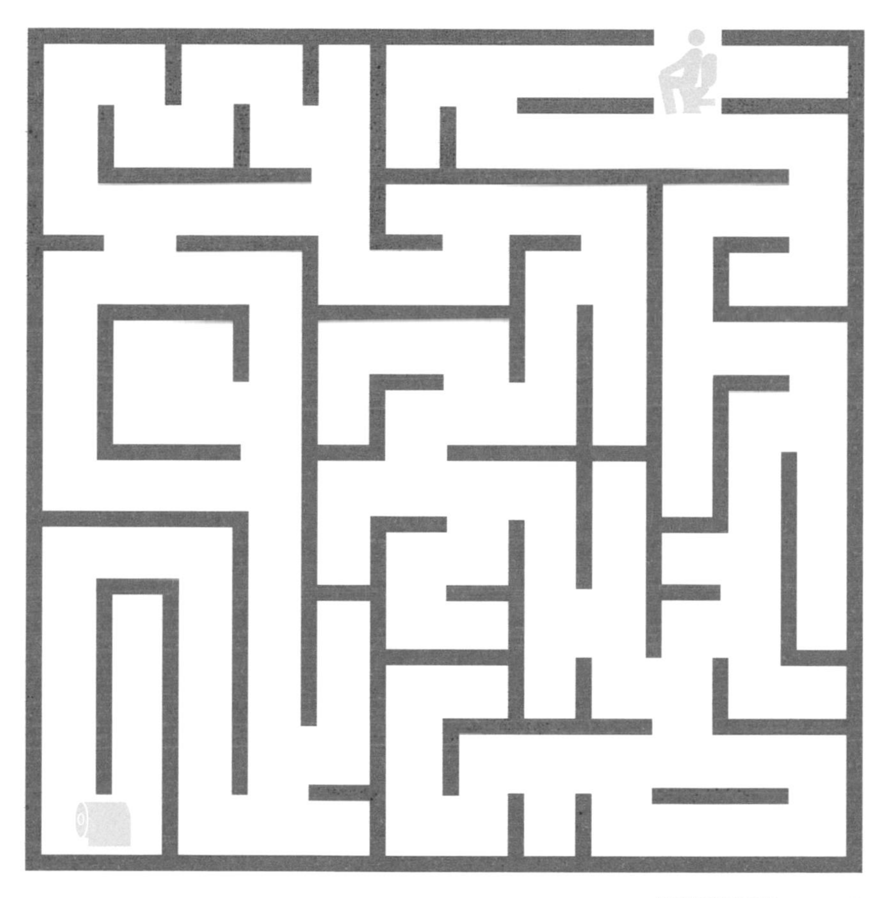

THIS PAIR ONLY APPEARS ONCE ON THE OPPOSITE PAGE

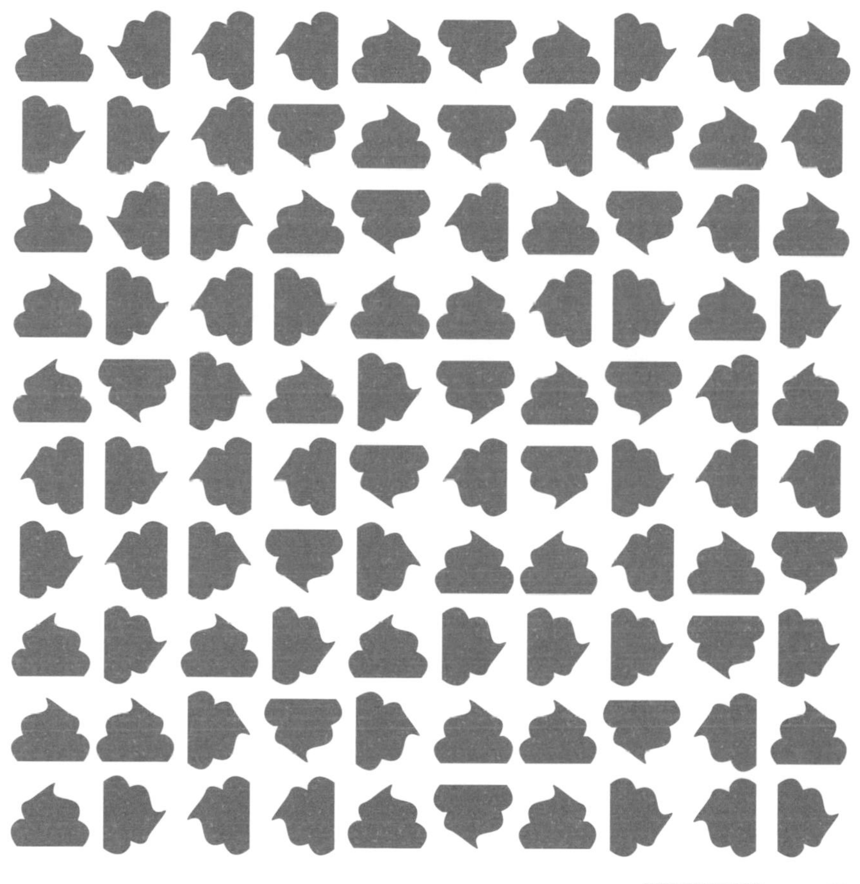

72.4%

27.6%

POO
FACT

WOMEN ARE MORE LIKELY TO SCRUNCH THE TOILET PAPER. MEN TEND TO BE FOLDERS.

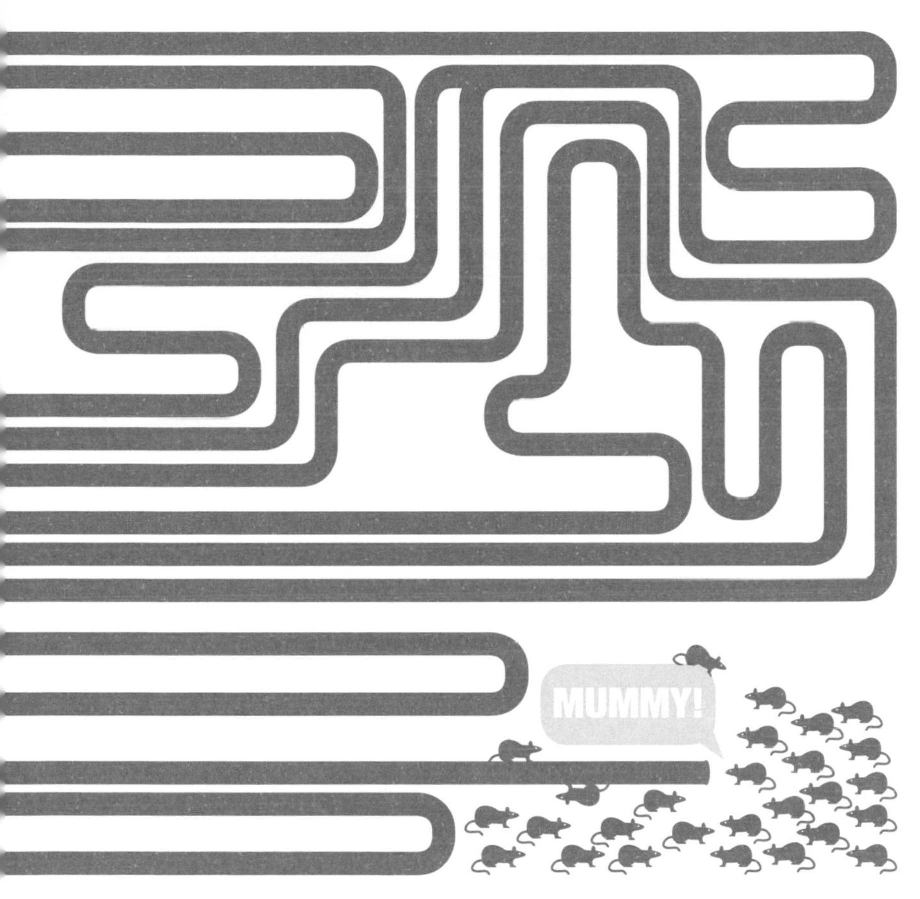

... WHILE YOU POO

POO FACT

A RAT CAN SURVIVE AFTER BEING FLUSHED DOWN A TOILET. IT CAN OFTEN COME BACK THE SAME WAY.

POO FACT

THE FIRST CUBICLE IN A PUBLIC TOILET IS THE LEAST USED – IT IS ALSO THE CLEANEST

POO

CRAP

DROPPING

STOOL

DUMP

MUCK

NUMBER TWO

SHIT

EXCREMENT

TURD

CACA

FAECES

F	A	E	C	E	S	D	U	M	P
H	N	L	B	E	S	R	O	U	A
S	U	C	U	X	Q	O	O	C	J
S	M	A	O	C	R	P	T	K	B
T	B	C	C	R	A	P	Y	O	S
O	E	A	N	E	Z	I	N	P	H
O	R	R	E	M	A	N	D	O	I
L	T	G	I	E	P	G	V	O	T
E	W	H	I	N	M	A	L	I	P
F	O	T	K	T	U	R	D	M	V

WHOSE POO?

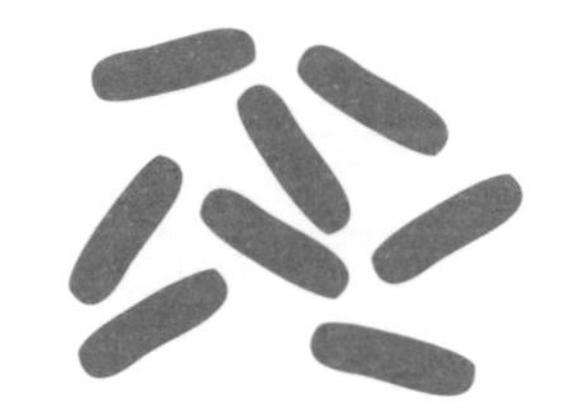

FIND THE VACANT TOILET

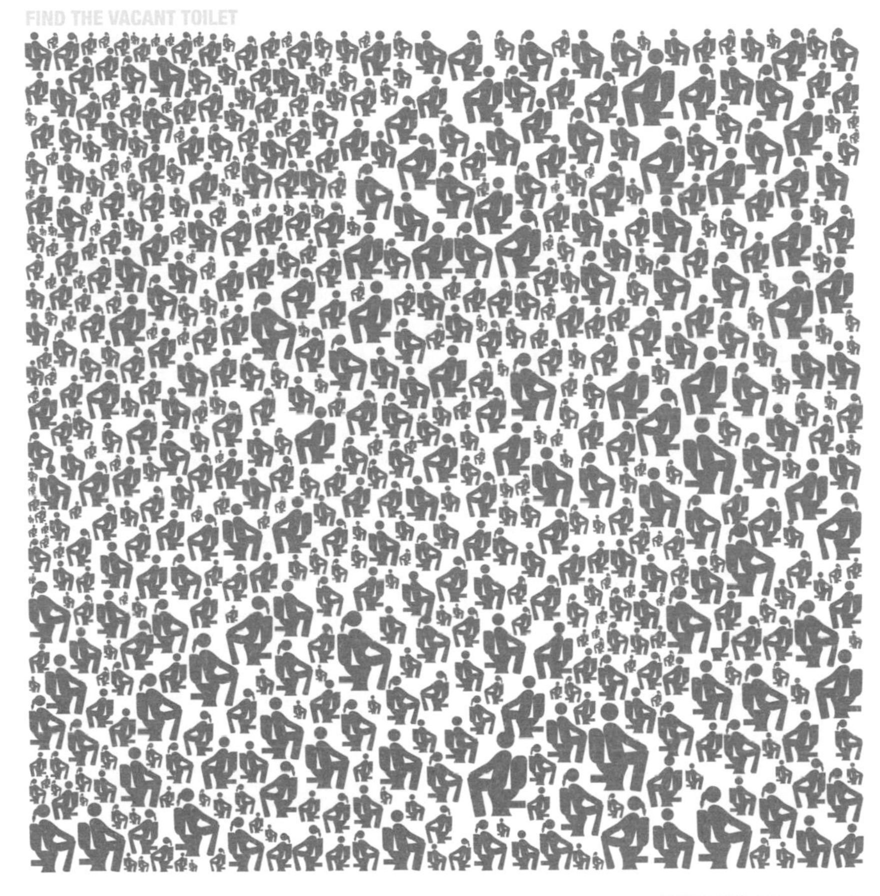

SPOT THE DIFFERENCE – THERE'S ONLY ONE!

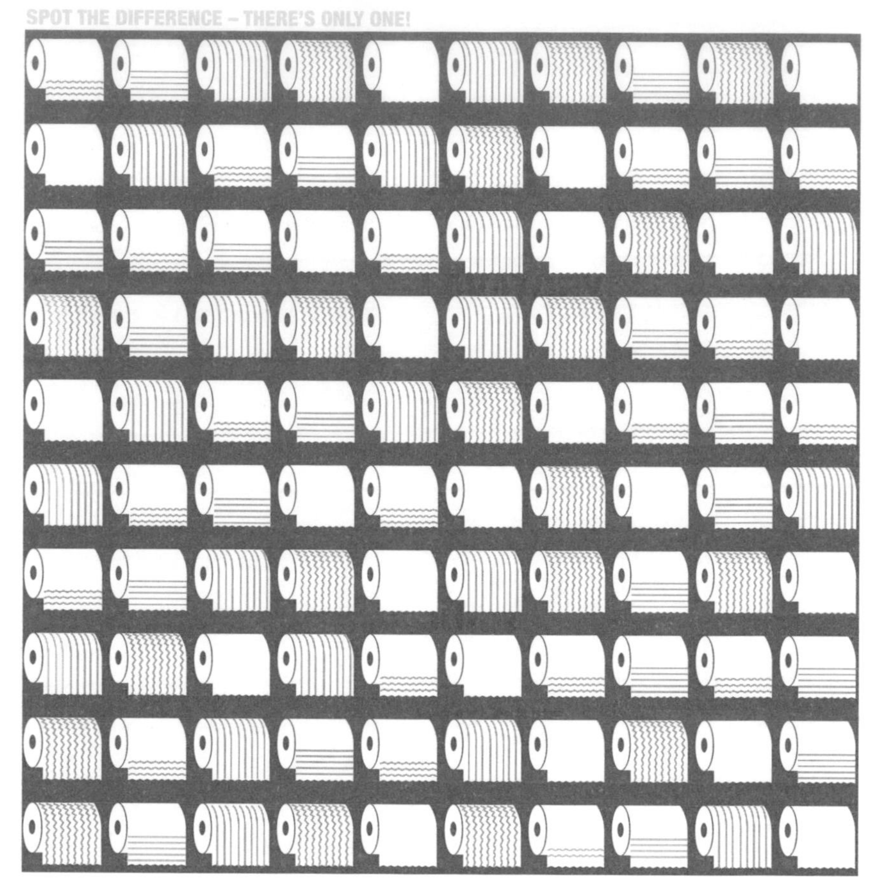

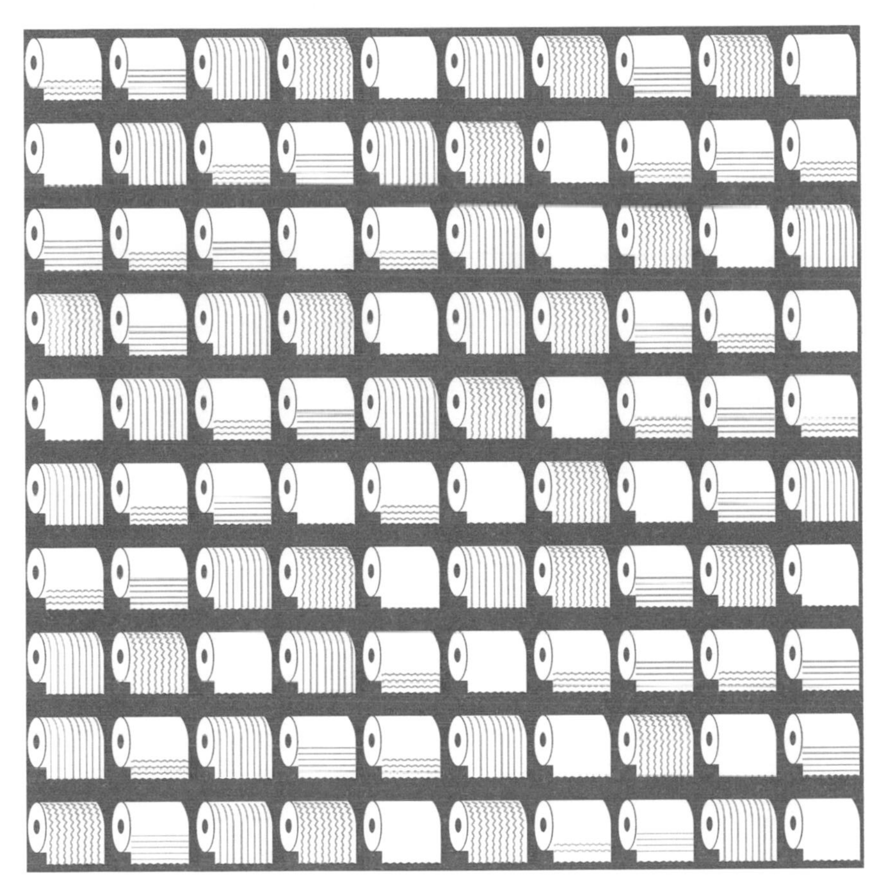

POO FACT

THE FLUSH HANDLE IN A PUBLIC TOILET CAN HAVE UP TO 40,000 GERMS PER SQUARE INCH

POO FACT

MOST TOILETS FLUSH
IN THE KEY OF E FLAT

WHOSE POO?

FIND THE BRUSH THE TOILET NEEDS A CLEAN!

POO FACT

POO SMELLS DUE TO SULPHUR-RICH COMPOUNDS INDOLE, SKATOLE, MERCAPTANS AND HYDROGEN SULPHIDE GAS

POO
FACT

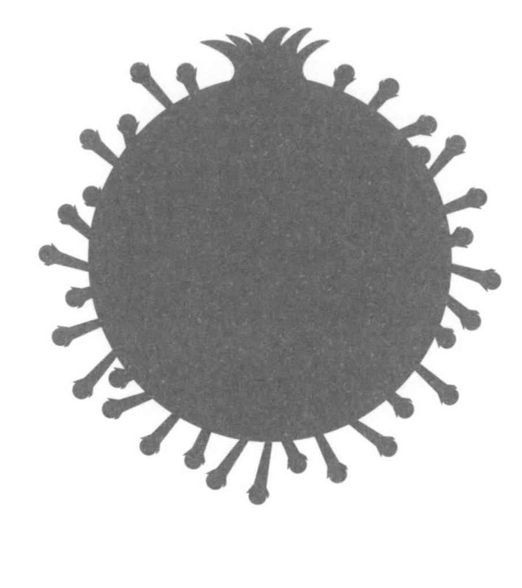

THE FIRST ATTEMPT AT MAKING TOILET AIR-FRESHENERS WERE POMEGRANATES STUDDED WITH CLOVES

TOILET
OUTHOUSE
LAVATORY
BOG
DUNNY
RESTROOM
KHAZI
PRIVY
JOHN
CAN
THRONE

A	Q	R	Y	J	O	H	N	Z	M
I	W	E	P	N	N	Y	U	L	L
B	G	S	O	T	D	V	C	A	N
O	U	T	H	O	U	S	E	V	T
G	B	R	J	I	N	S	J	A	H
X	C	O	R	L	N	Y	I	T	R
D	E	O	S	E	Y	P	K	O	O
T	A	M	I	T	K	Z	H	R	N
P	R	O	U	P	R	I	V	Y	E
N	I	A	P	K	H	A	Z	I	G

COMPLETE THE SEQUENCE

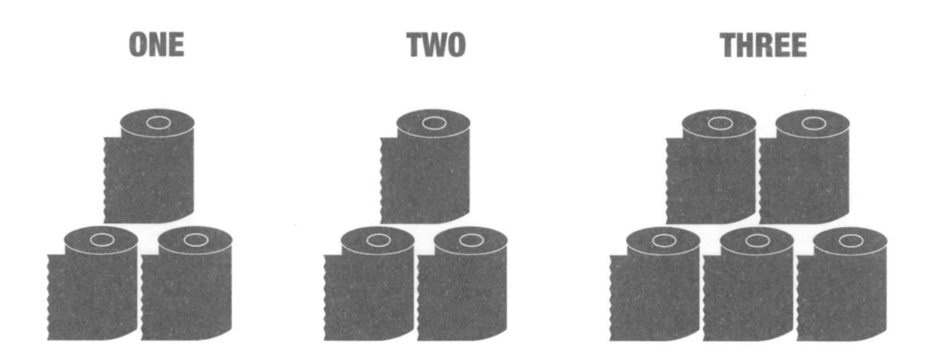

FOUR

FIVE

SIX

?

THIS PAIR ONLY APPEARS ONCE ON THE OPPOSITE PAGE

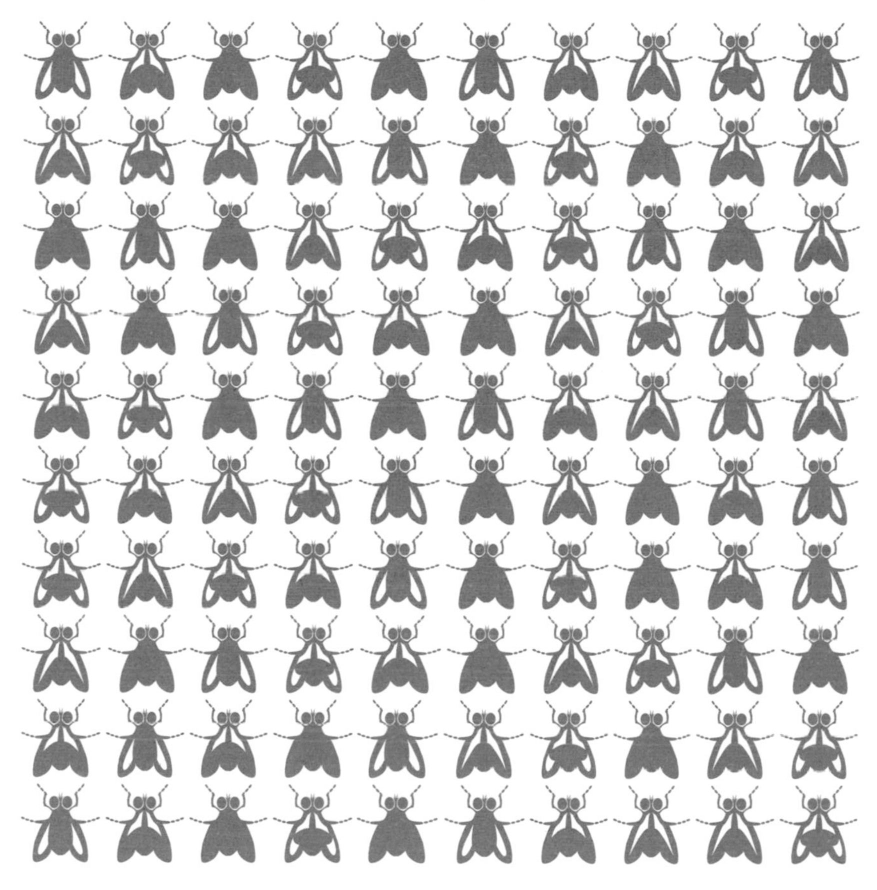

POO FACT

THE ROMANS USED WATER-SOAKED SPONGES ON THE END OF STICKS INSTEAD OF TOILET PAPER

POO
FACT

ON 25 OCTOBER 1760 KING GEORGE II DIED FALLING OFF A TOILET

POO FACT
1880

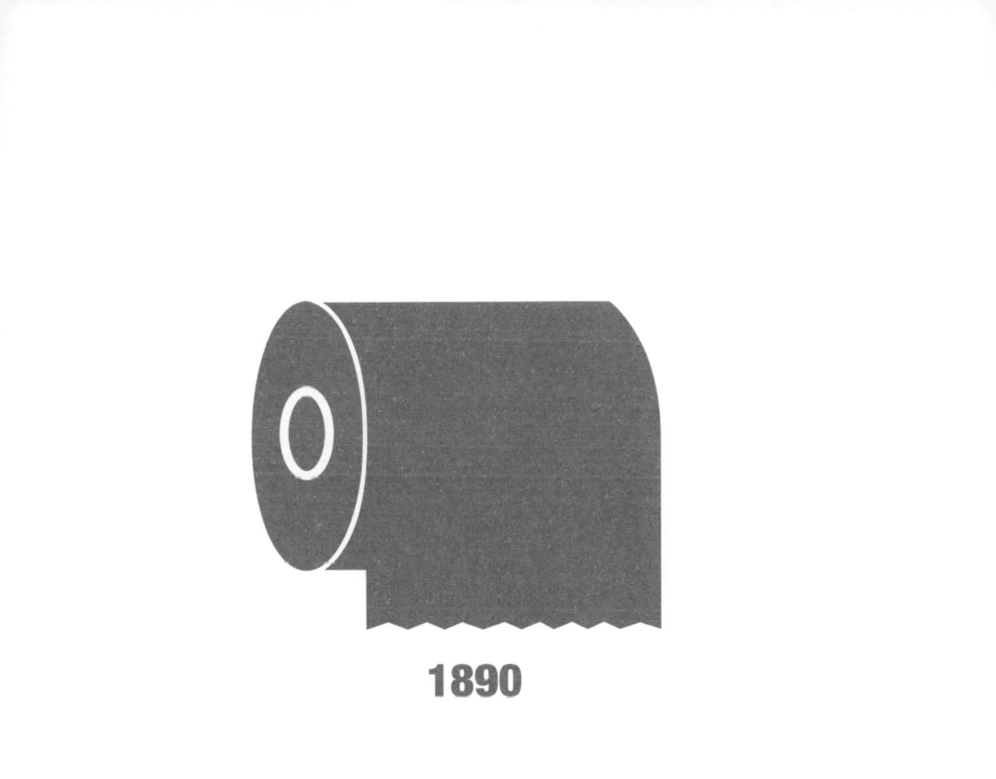
1890

FIND MY TWIN!

MR FLY IS ON HIS LAST LEGS. HE ONLY HAS SIX FLIGHTS LEFT IN HIM. CAN YOU HELP HIM TAKE A NIBBLE FROM ALL 15 TURDS IN ONLY SIX STRAIGHT FLIGHTS BEFORE HE DIES?

... WHILE YOU POO

SPOT THE DIFFERENCE - THERE'S ONLY ONE!

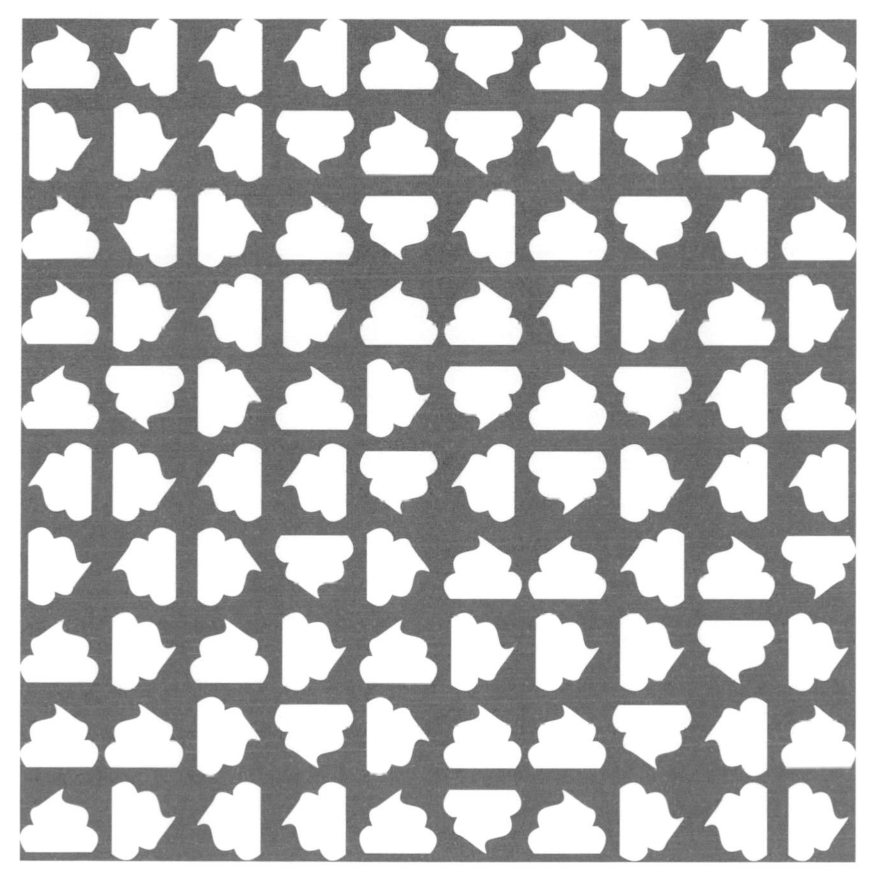

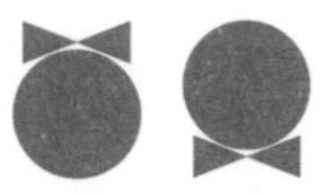

THIS PAIR ONLY APPEARS ONCE ON THE OPPOSITE PAGE

3 lb/DAY

300 lb/DAY

THESE SHELVES OF TOILET PAPER ARE STRAIGHT. HONEST.

POO FACT

33% FLUSH THE TOILET WHILE SITTING ON IT

BUM

BUTT

ARSE

BOOTY

REAR

BACKSIDE

BEHIND

BOTTOM

TUSH

RUMP

D	A	I	E	B	O	O	T	Y	U
B	R	A	B	U	M	T	F	I	B
I	S	I	A	T	I	T	B	G	E
C	E	G	C	T	S	T	O	W	H
H	I	M	K	I	R	I	T	I	I
I	T	U	S	H	T	G	T	O	N
J	A	O	I	I	L	R	O	N	D
E	I	U	D	K	V	K	M	P	M
I	P	R	E	A	R	I	W	T	S
Q	E	O	R	R	U	M	P	X	L

POO FACT

FARTS CONTAIN THE FLAMMABLE GASES METHANE, HYDROGEN SULPHIDE AND HYDROGEN

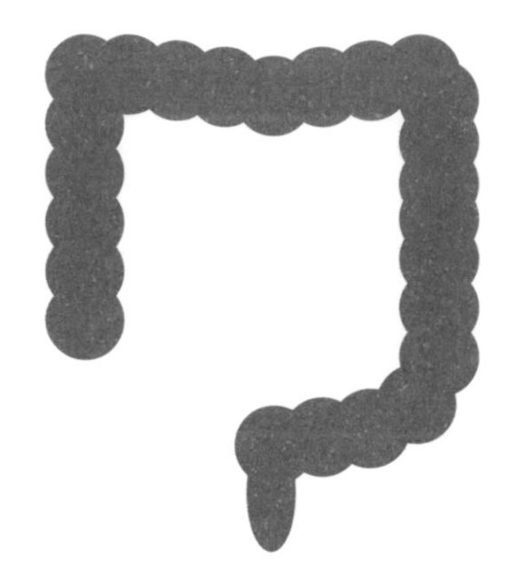

THE SHAPE OF YOUR POO DEPENDS ON THE TIME IT HAS SPENT IN YOUR COLON

TYPES 1 & 2 – CONSTIPATION
TYPES 3 & 4 – NORMAL
TYPE 5 - HEADING TOWARDS DIARRHOEA
TYPE 6 & 7 – DIARRHOEA

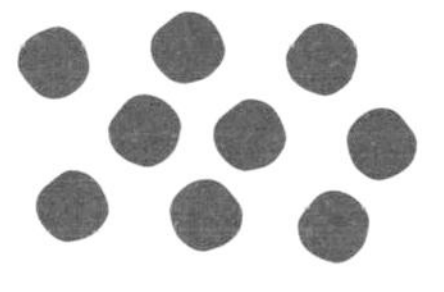

TYPE 1

LIKE BALLS OF OVERCOOKED SAUSAGE
PASS DIFFICULTY 3
(1 EASY, 3 DIFFICULT)

TYPE 2

LIKE A LUMPY SAUSAGE
PASS DIFFICULTY 2.5

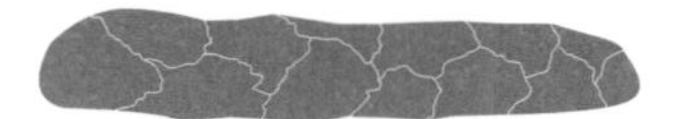

TYPE 3

LIKE A CRACKED SAUSAGE
PASS DIFFICULTY 2

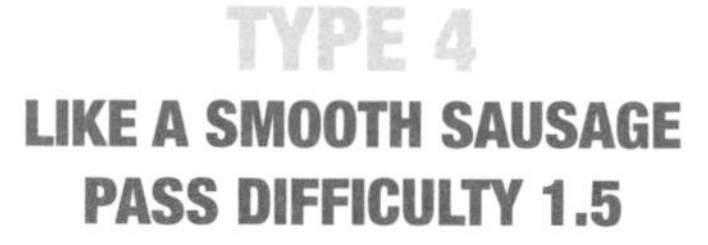

TYPE 4

LIKE A SMOOTH SAUSAGE
PASS DIFFICULTY 1.5

TYPE 5

LIKE A SOFT CUT-UP SAUSAGE
PASS DIFFICULTY 1

TYPE 6

LIKE A MASHED UP SAUSAGE
PASS DIFFICULTY 1

TYPE 7

LIKE A LIQUIDISED SAUSAGE
PASS DIFFICULTY -4

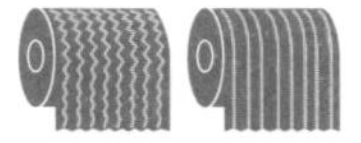

THIS PAIR ONLY APPEARS ONCE ON THE OPPOSITE PAGE

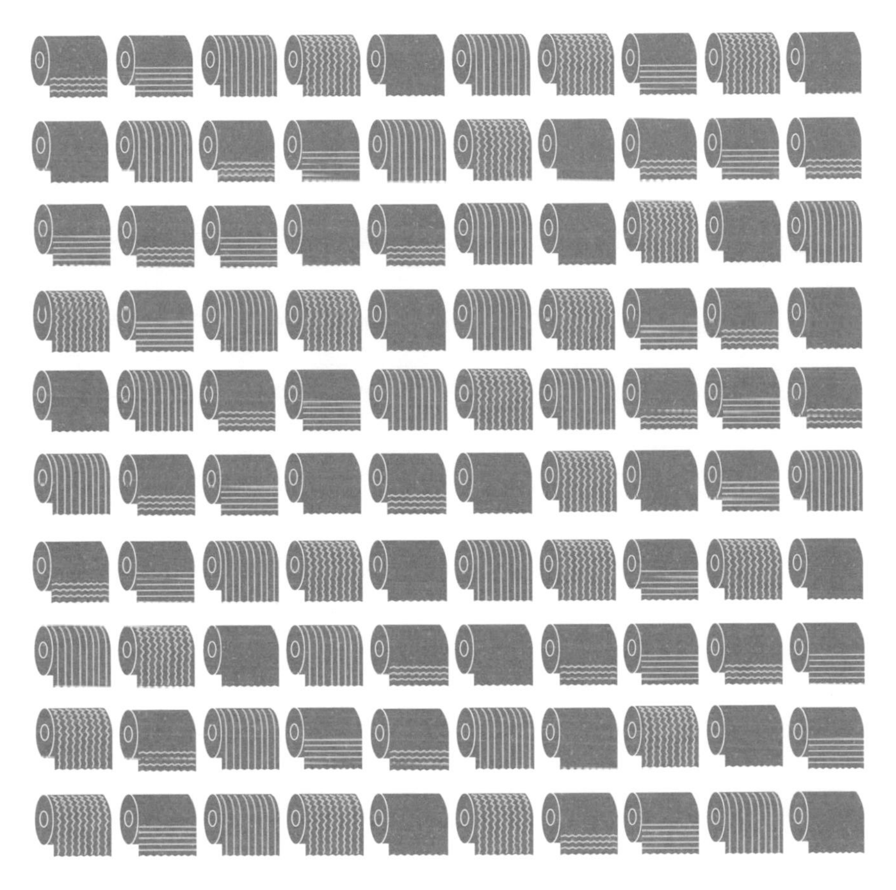

... WHILE YOU POO

SPOT THE DIFFERENCE – THERE'S ONLY ONE!

POO FACT

THE AVERAGE PERSON SPENDS THREE YEARS OF THEIR LIFE ON THE TOILET

PEE

WEE

WAZ

TINKLE

URINATE

PISS

TAKE A LEAK

NUMBER ONE

A	W	T	Z	E	F	A	P	Q	G
J	N	U	M	B	E	R	O	N	E
I	O	U	R	I	N	A	T	E	T
Y	T	B	H	P	W	W	E	E	I
C	U	J	W	E	Z	O	R	A	N
Y	T	A	K	E	A	L	E	A	K
M	P	W	D	W	S	U	M	K	L
R	I	E	P	I	S	S	P	W	E
U	W	O	V	S	E	W	A	Z	L
A	M	B	Y	T	H	W	Z	S	M

FIND THE BABY WITH THE DIRTY NAPPY!

THIS PAIR ONLY APPEARS ONCE ON THE OPPOSITE PAGE

... WHILE YOU POO

SPOT THE DIFFERENCE – THERE'S ONLY ONE!

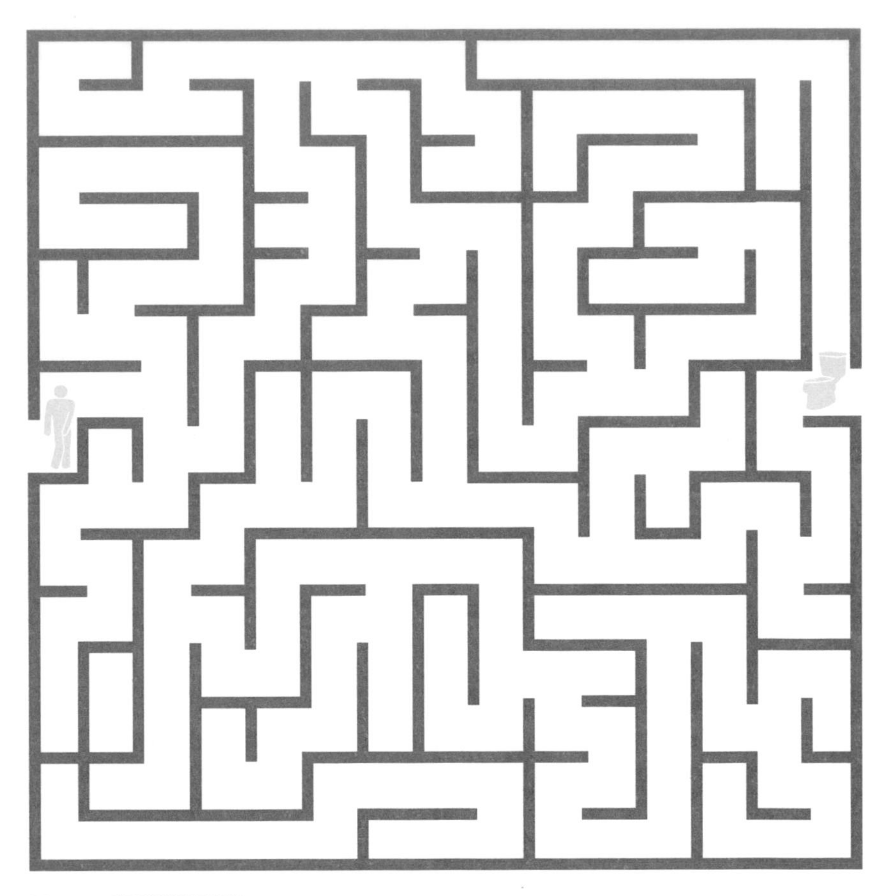

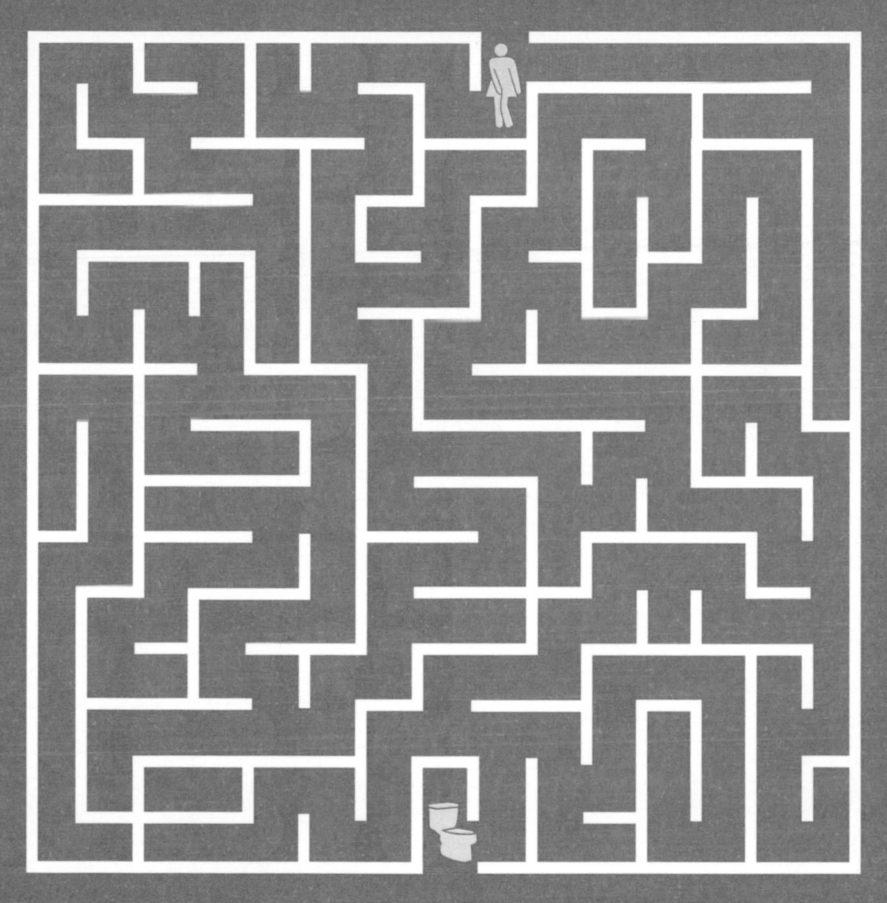

POO FACT

THERE CAN BE AS MANY AS 100 PARASITE EGGS, 1,000 PARASITE CYSTS, 1,000,000 BACTERIA AND 10,000,000 VIRUSES IN 1 GRAM OF HUMAN POO

POO FACT

THE AVERAGE LENGTH OF A TWO-PLY ROLL OF TOILET PAPER IS 57 METRES

POO FACT

11
1
10
2
8
4
7
5

THE AVERAGE PERSON VISITS THE TOILET 2,500 TIMES A YEAR – ABOUT SIX TO EIGHT TIMES A DAY

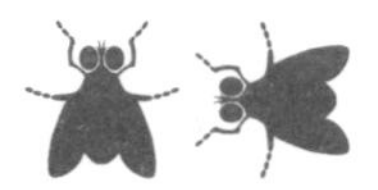

THIS PAIR ONLY APPEARS ONCE ON THE OPPOSITE PAGE

POO FACT

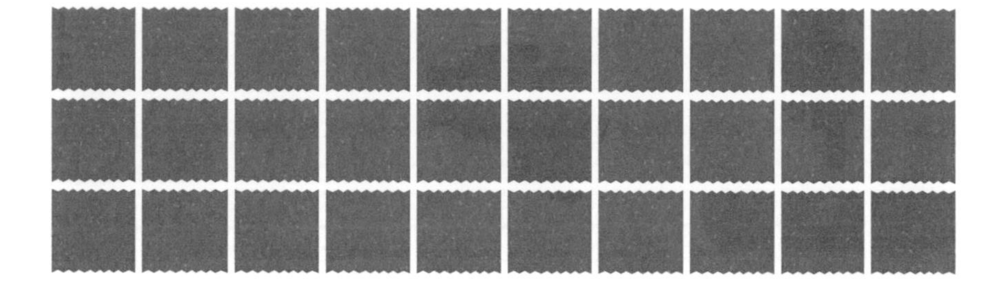

ON AVERAGE WE USE 57 SHEETS OF TOILET PAPER EACH PER DAY

ENTER
UNZIP
SIT
POO
WIPE
FLUSH
WASH
DRY
SPRAY
LEAVE

Q	V	E	N	T	E	R	E	W	V
A	W	R	I	D	L	E	A	V	E
F	A	G	P	O	O	T	S	E	O
I	S	Y	H	W	F	W	I	P	E
M	H	A	N	C	I	G	T	B	M
S	I	N	E	F	L	U	S	H	O
D	R	Y	B	I	C	N	A	H	P
E	N	I	A	P	D	Z	T	X	I
K	S	P	R	A	Y	I	O	L	U
P	S	I	U	R	T	P	U	X	L

ANSWERS

P6-7

P9

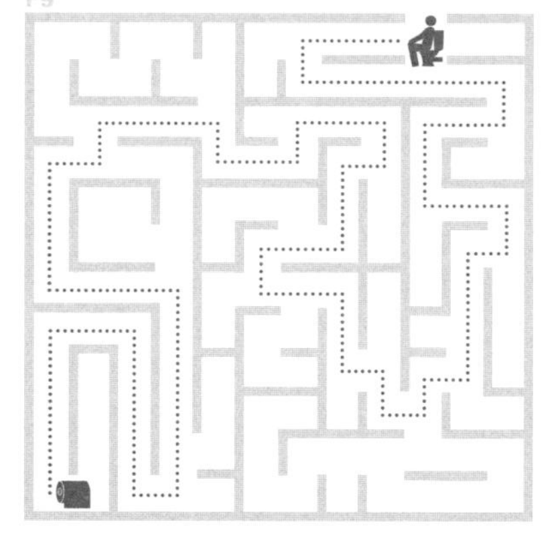

P10-11

P14-15

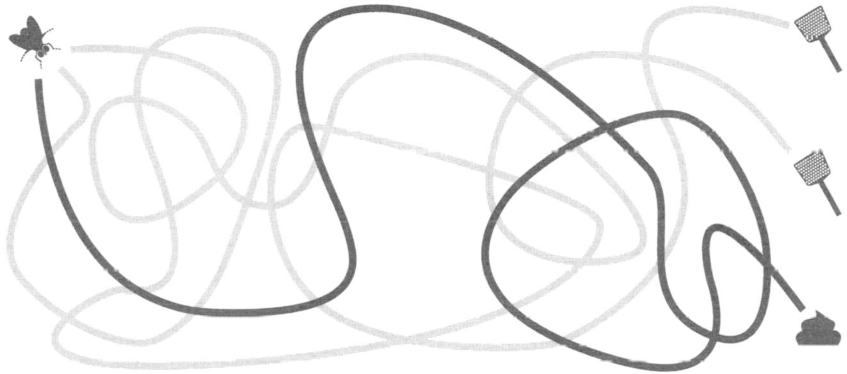

P18-19

MUMMY!

P24-25

P28-29

P26 **RAT. DROPPINGS ARE ABOUT 10MM LONG WITH BLUNT ENDS**

P34 **MOUSE. SAME SIZE AS GRAINS OF RICE WITH POINTED ENDS**

P27

P35

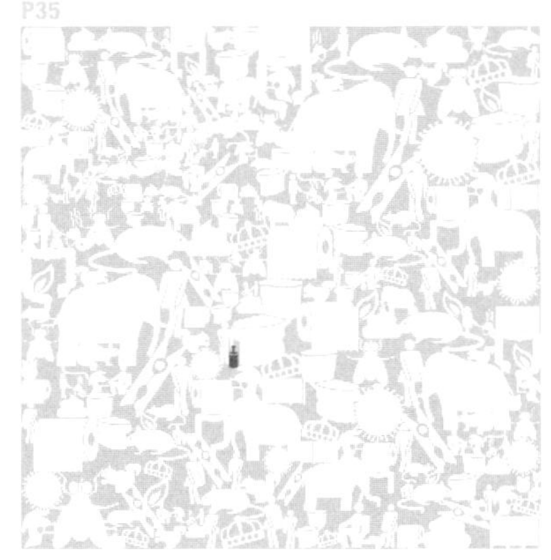

P40-41

P44-45

P42-43

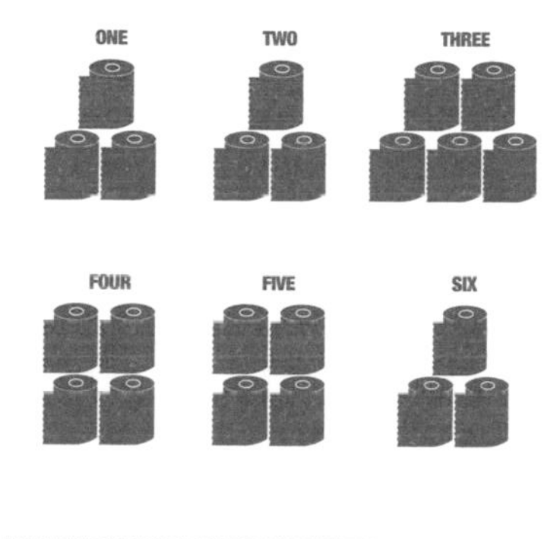

THE AMOUNT OF TOILET ROLLS IS THE NUMBER OF LETTERS IN THE WORD

P52-53

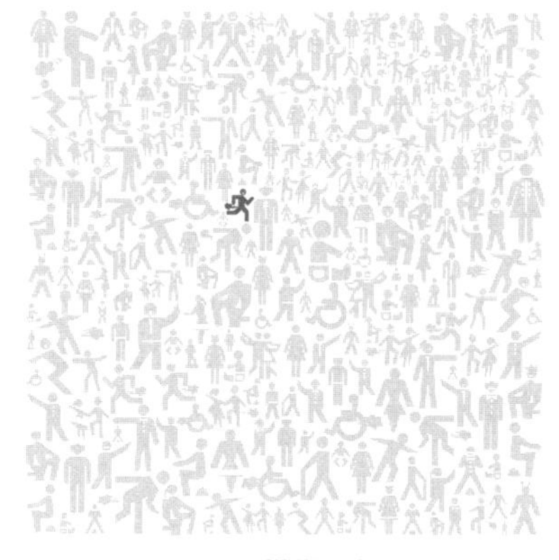

P54-55

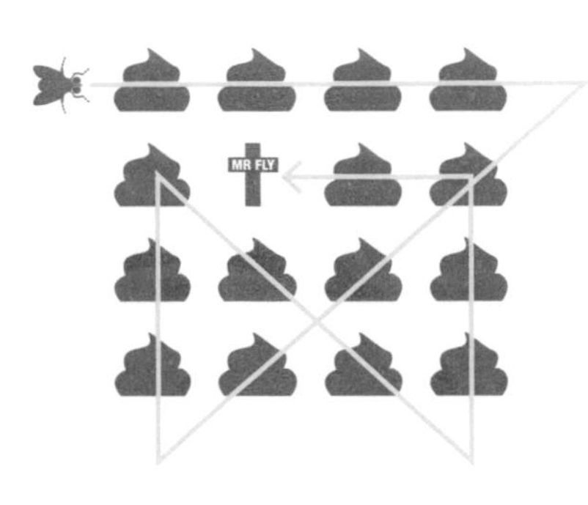

P58-59

P56-57

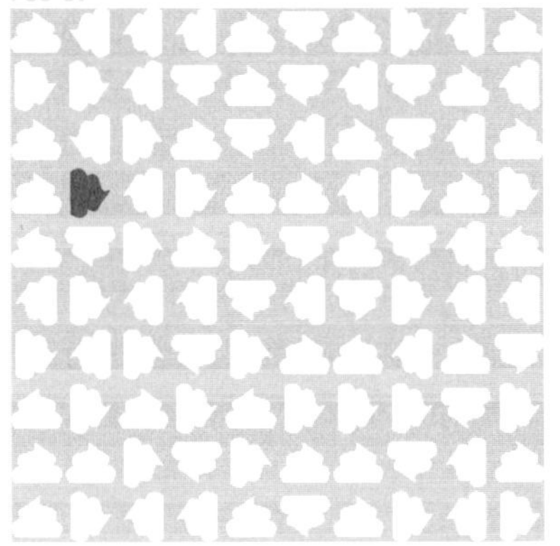

P66-67

D A I E B O O T Y U
B R A B U M T F I B
I S I A T I T B G E
C E G C T S T O W H
H I M K I R I T I I
I T U S H T G T O N
J A O I I L R O N D
E I U D K V K M P M
I P R E A R I W T S
Q E O R R U M P X L

P74-75

P76-77

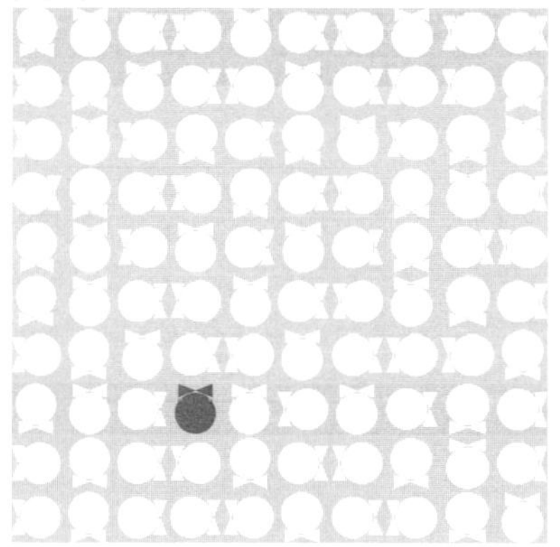

P80-81

A W T Z E F A P Q G
J N U M B E R O N E
I O U R I N A T E T
Y T B H P W W E E I
C U J W E Z O R A N
Y T A K E A L E A K
M P W D W S U M K L
R I E P I S S P W E
U W O V S E W A Z L
A M B Y T H W Z S M

P82-83

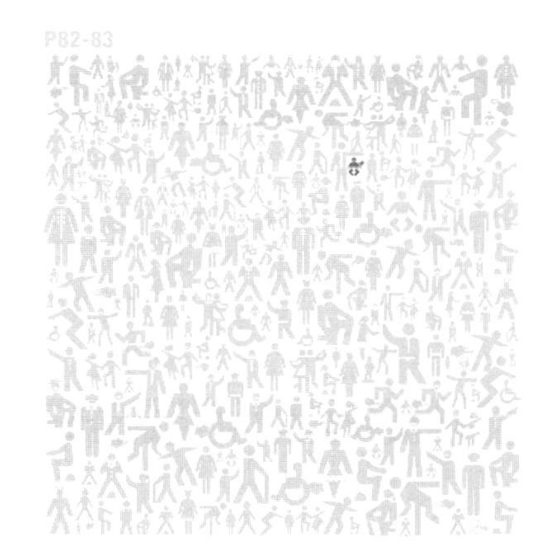

P84-85

P86-87

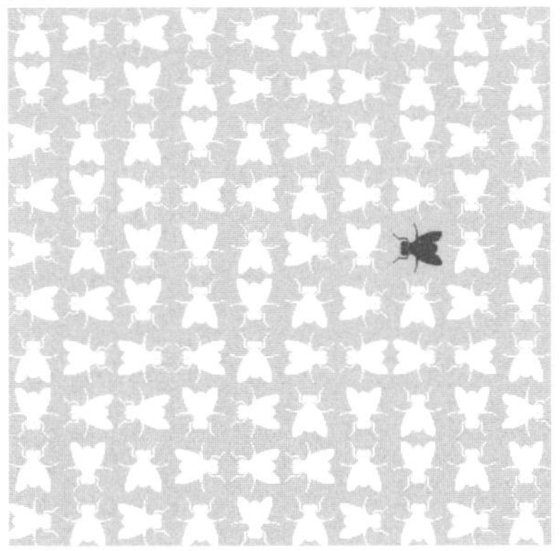

P88

P89

P92-93

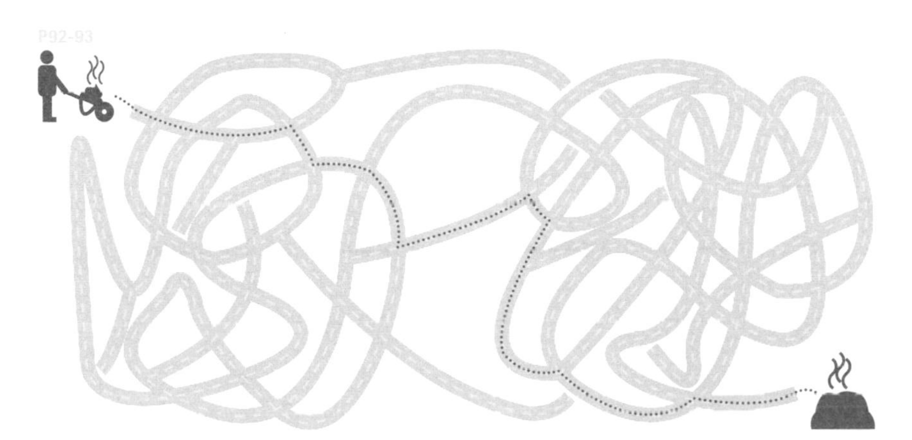

P98-99

P102-103

ALL DONE?

THANK YOU!